Tales from the Serengeti

Thabo and Kanoni

Thabo, the rhinoceros,
was quite a
sad
fellow. Like most
rhinoceros, he had very
poor eyesight and
so lived all **alone**
in the wild.
That was the reason
for his **sad** situation,
for he longed to
have friends.
There were just
none he could see.

On the rare occasion
when Thabo accidently
bumped
into a herd of friendly
zebras or wildebeest,
it was not very long
before he would find
himself running in the
wrong
direction with a
completely
different crowd!

"It's hopeless,"
he said one day to
a large acacia tree.
"You are the only
friend that I have.
That is, of course, only
as long as I stay right
here, for I can see
no one else
to talk to."

"That sounds good to me!" came a small voice from the tree. "For I, too, am lonely and could surely use a friend."

Thabo
jumped
back startled
and surprised,
"What? Pardon me!
Mr. Tree, did you say
something to **me**?"

"It was **me**, not the tree,"
laughed a small tickbird.
"Your tale sounds all
too familiar to me.
So listen, I, Kanoni,
will be your friend
if you will be mine.
Friendship
just works best
that way."

"That would be splendid!" the rhinoceros exclaimed. "My name is Thabo and my **poor** eyesight is to blame for my lack of companions."

"Well," replied
Kanoni,
"It is not my eyesight,
but these terribly
short wings
that have
left me behind
and up here
in this tree."

"This is a choice
friendship,"
Thabo then said.
"For I can
ramble
on for hours
without needing
a break. With your
keen eyes,
you can perch up
front on my
horn and tell me
which way to go."

"A great choice,
indeed," Kanoni said as
he fluttered down.
"With your lumbering
legs and my
farsighted eyes,
a **great team**
we will be.
We just can't go wrong!"

It only took a couple of minutes before practice made perfect and they were off scattering

dust

across the wide African plains. Now and then, they joined up with migrating herds making many new

friends

before leaving on new adventures.

After many years of living happily, Thabo said to Kanoni one day, "I am so glad to have met you under that tree so long ago. For you were right that day when you said, '**Friendships** work best when they go both ways!'"